DeltaScienceReaders™

Electrical Conne...

CONTENTS

What Is Electric Charge?

▲ **Figure 1** A stove converts electric energy into heat energy that cooks our food.

VOCABULARY

electric energy	charging by friction
electric charge	
atom	separation of charge
electron	charging by conduction
proton	
neutron	charging by induction
nucleus	
ion	induced charge
static charge	electroscope
static electricity	static discharge
conductor	
insulator	grounding
electric force	lightning
electric field	lightning rod

Most of us rely on electricity in almost every minute of every day. Many people use the word *electricity* to describe **electric energy.** Energy is the ability to do work or cause changes (Figure 1). A light bulb converts electric energy into light energy. Where does electric energy come from? The answer begins with charged particles.

Electric charge is a basic property of matter. You may know that all matter is made up of tiny building blocks called **atoms.** Atoms are composed of smaller, subatomic particles called protons, neutrons, and electrons. An **electron** has a negative (–) electric charge. A **proton** has a positive (+) electric charge. A **neutron** has no charge. Neutrons are neutral. Protons and neutrons make up the center, or **nucleus,** of an atom. Electrons move quickly around the nucleus (Figure 2).

The sum of all the charges in an atom determines the atom's overall, or net, charge. For example, when the number of electrons in an atom is equal to the number of protons, the atom has a net charge of zero. The electric charges of the subatomic particles are balanced. When the number of electrons and protons in an atom is not equal, the atom has either a net positive or a net negative charge. An atom with a net positive or net negative charge is called an **ion.**

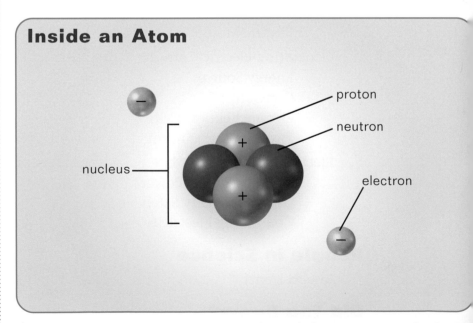

Inside an Atom

proton

neutron

nucleus

electron

▲ **Figure 2** Atoms contain negatively charged electrons, positively charged protons, and neutral neutrons. The atom shown is a helium atom. It has a net charge of zero.

Static Charge

Most of the time, materials or objects are electrically neutral. The number of electrons and the number of protons in an object are equal. However, electrons can be transferred from one object to another object. If a neutral object gains electrons, the object will have more negative charges than positive charges. This excess of negative charge causes the object to be negatively charged (Figure 3). If a neutral object loses electrons, the object will have an excess of positive charge. The object will be positively charged. An object's excess of positive or negative charge is called **static charge.** The buildup of charge on an object is sometimes referred to as **static electricity.** Most static charges are trillions of times larger than the charge of a single electron or proton.

Depending on how a material's electrons behave, the material can be classified as either a conductor or an insulator. A **conductor** is a material whose electrons are held loosely. They can move easily from one atom to another. The copper in a wire is classified as a conductor. Electrons move easily along it. An **insulator** is a material whose electrons cannot move easily. Rubber and glass are insulators.

Electric Force

All charged materials or objects exert a force called **electric force.** Materials with like static charges repel, or push each other away (Figure 4). For example, two positively charged materials repel each other. The same is true for two negatively charged materials. On the other hand, materials with opposite, or unlike, charges attract, or pull each other closer. For example, a negatively charged material and a positively charged material attract each other.

Recall that the nucleus of an atom is composed of positively charged protons and neutral neutrons. So the nucleus as a whole has a positive charge. The electrons around the nucleus are negatively charged. The electric force between the positively charged nucleus and the negatively charged electrons holds the atom together.

Charged objects do not have to touch each other for electric force to act between them. This is because electric force can act over a distance. The space around a charged object where electric force acts is called an **electric field.** Electric force acts between two objects when their electric fields interact.

Static Charge

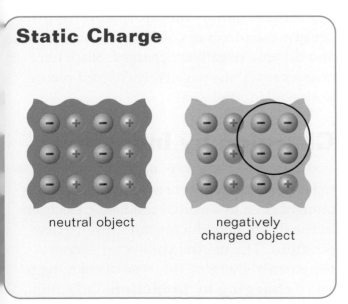

neutral object

negatively charged object

▲ **Figure 3** An object with an equal number of protons and electrons is neutral. An object with more electrons than protons is negatively charged.

Electric Force

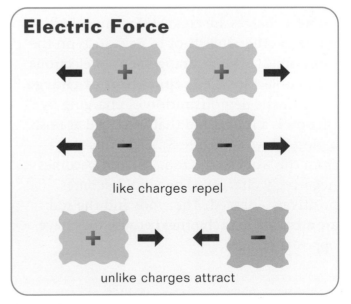

like charges repel

unlike charges attract

▲ **Figure 4** Electric force causes charged objects to interact in certain ways. Objects with like charges repel, or push each other away. Objects with unlike charges attract each other.

The size of the electric force between two charged materials depends on two factors. First, the size of the force depends on the size of the individual charges—greater charges produce greater force. Second, the size of the force depends on the distance between the charges. As the distance between the charges increases, the force decreases.

Charging by Friction

One way objects can become charged is by rubbing together. When two neutral objects rub together, electrons are transferred from one object to the other. This type of charging is called **charging by friction.**

Have you ever experienced "static cling"? As clothes tumble in a dryer, they rub together. Some clothes become positively charged and others become negatively charged. Since opposite charges attract, the positively charged clothes stick to the negatively charged clothes. Charging by friction works best if the two objects are insulators and the air around them is dry.

Charging by friction gives two neutral materials opposite charges when they are rubbed together. It is important to note that no new charges are created. Existing charges move to other objects or to new areas on the same object. This rearrangement of electrons on an object is called **separation of charge.**

A classic demonstration of charging by friction is a rubber rod that is rubbed against a piece of wool (Figure 5). Electrons move from the wool to the rod. The rod becomes negatively charged. The wool becomes positively charged. The wool and the rod are attracted to each other because they have opposite charges.

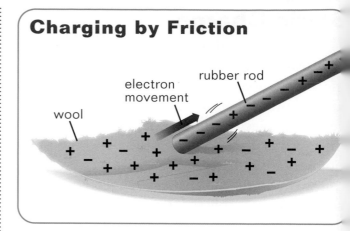

Charging by Friction

▲ **Figure 5** The wool and the rubber rod were electrically neutral before they were rubbed together. What net charge does the wool have now? How about the rubber rod?

Charging by Conduction

Another way neutral objects can become charged is by coming in contact with an already charged object. When a charged object touches a neutral object, electrons are transferred to the neutral object. This kind of charging is called **charging by conduction.** Objects that are charged by conduction have the same charge as the object that was used to charge them.

Suppose you touch a negatively charged rubber rod to a pile of neutral paper confetti. The confetti quickly flies apart. This happens because the pieces of confetti gain electrons and become negatively charged. Since like charges repel, the negatively charged pieces push one another away.

Charging by Induction

Contact is not always necessary for objects to become charged. When a charged object is brought close to a neutral conductor, electrons in the neutral conductor can move to new positions. The neutral conductor becomes temporarily charged. This type of charging is called **charging by induction.** Induction causes a material to have areas of both negative and positive charge. The areas of charge caused by induction are called **induced charges.**

Charging by induction causes an object to have charge that is opposite to the charge that is brought near it.

Suppose you rub a balloon against your hair, charging the balloon by friction. The balloon becomes negatively charged. Now suppose you hold the balloon near a neutral wall and let go. The negative charge of the balloon induces a region of positive charge on the wall (Figure 6). The attractive force between the negative charges on the balloon and the induced positive charge on the wall will make the balloon temporarily stick to the wall.

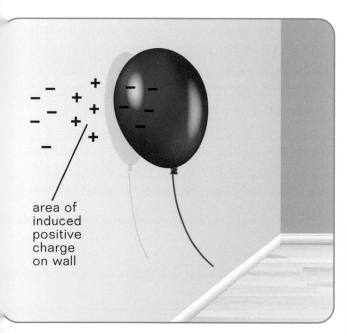

area of induced positive charge on wall

▲ **Figure 6** A negatively charged balloon can induce a positive charge on a small section of a wall.

Detecting Charge

An **electroscope** (Figure 7-A) is an instrument that detects electric charge. One type of electroscope has a glass flask and a rubber stopper, both of which are insulators. The electroscope also has a metal knob, metal stem, and two very thin metal strips called leaves, all of which are conductors.

Normally, the metal leaves of an electroscope hang straight down. They hang down because electrons and protons are evenly distributed throughout the metal knob, stem, and leaves. The electroscope has a neutral charge.

Suppose a negatively charged object is brought close to the electroscope's metal knob, but does not touch it (Figure 7-B). The negative charge on the object induces a positive charge on the knob. Electrons in the knob are pushed toward the stem. These electrons push electrons from the stem into the leaves. Both leaves become negatively charged. Since like charges repel, the leaves spread apart. If the charged object is moved away from the knob, the electrons in the electroscope move back to their original places. The leaves become neutral and return to their hanging position.

The same results occur if a positively charged object is brought near a neutral electroscope. The positive charge on the object induces a negative charge on the knob. Electrons from the leaves are attracted and move up the stem. The leaves become positively charged and move apart. So the leaves of a simple electroscope move apart in response to either a negative or a positive charge. Therefore, an electroscope can be used to detect a charge, but it cannot determine the type of charge.

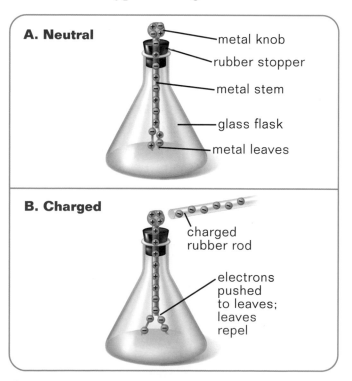

A. Neutral — metal knob — rubber stopper — metal stem — glass flask — metal leaves

B. Charged — charged rubber rod — electrons pushed to leaves; leaves repel

▲ **Figure 7** The metal knob, stem, and leaves of an electroscope are normally neutral. The leaves separate when both have the same charge.

Static Discharge

A charged object will lose its static charge over time. Recall the charged balloon that stuck to the wall. The balloon will lose electrons as molecules and charged particles in the air strike it. As the balloon becomes neutral again, the force of attraction between the balloon and the wall weakens. Eventually the balloon no longer sticks to the wall. This loss of static charge is called **static discharge.**

Static discharge also can happen quickly. One way is through a process called grounding. Connecting a charged object to a much larger conducting material is called **grounding.** Through grounding, a charged object will return to a neutral state.

Have you ever felt a slight shock when you touched a metal doorknob after walking across a carpet? As you walk across a carpet, electrons rub off the carpet onto the bottom of your shoes. This gives you a negative charge. When you touch the doorknob, you are grounded. Electrons rapidly jump from your hand to the doorknob. You may feel a slight shock and see a small spark. You now have an even balance of electrons and protons and return to a neutral state.

Lightning is an example of a powerful static discharge. Lightning can occur between clouds and the ground or between two clouds. The movement of ice particles inside a cloud causes friction. A separation of charge occurs in the cloud, with positive charges on the top of the cloud and negative charges on the bottom. The negative charges induce areas of positive charge on the ground below. Lightning occurs as a short, rapid flow of charge between the clouds and Earth.

A **lightning rod** is a device that protects buildings from lightning strikes. The rod is a grounded metal conductor attached to the building by insulators. The rod sticks up into the air above the building. During a storm, the negative charge of the cloud induces a positive charge on the ground, building, and rod. Because the rod is closer to the clouds, it is more likely to be struck by lightning. When struck, the rod conducts the electrons down a wire and into the ground (Figure 8). The insulators keep the static discharge from passing through the building.

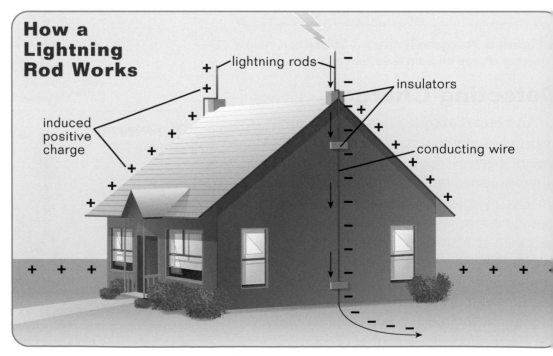

► **Figure 8** The lightning rod on the right is carrying static discharge from a lightning strike away from the house. Electrons are conducted safely through the rod, down a low-resistance conducting wire, and into the ground.

How a Lightning Rod Works

lightning rods
insulators
induced positive charge
conducting wire

What Is Electric Current?

Electric energy is the energy a charge has because it is in an electric field or electric current. An **electric current** is a continuous flow of electric charge. More precisely, current is the rate at which electric charge is flowing. A lightning strike is a large flow of charge that lasts for a short time. A smaller, continuous flow of charge is more useful. We use electric current to operate electronic devices such as kitchen appliances, televisions, and stereos.

Electric current can pass through many materials, but most materials limit current. A material's ability to limit current is called **resistance.** An insulator has very great resistance. A conductor has very little resistance.

Electric Circuits

An **electric circuit** is a path for electric current. Electric energy is transferred through an electric circuit. Electric circuits have three main parts: a conducting path, a source of electric energy, and a resistor (Figure 9).

Wire is one type of conducting path. In a typical household circuit, the wire is made of copper metal surrounded by a plastic coating. The copper is a conductor and the plastic is an insulator. This type of wire is called insulated wire.

A battery is one source of electric energy. A **battery** converts chemical energy to electric energy.

A light bulb is one type of resistor. A **resistor** is a device that resists the flow of current and changes electric energy into another form of energy. The light bulb changes electric energy into heat and light energy.

The light bulb shown in Figure 9 stays lit because the circuit is closed. A **closed circuit** has a complete path for current to follow.

Closed Circuit

▲ **Figure 9** What type of conducting path do electrons follow in this simple closed circuit?

READ TO UNDERSTAND

- What are the three parts of an electric circuit?
- How is the current in a circuit calculated?
- How are series and parallel circuits different?

VOCABULARY

electric current	electric potential
resistance	potential difference
electric circuit	voltage
battery	volt (V)
resistor	ampere (A)
closed circuit	ohm (Ω)
switch	Ohm's law
open circuit	series circuit
circuit diagram	parallel circuit
gravitational potential energy	

Open Circuit

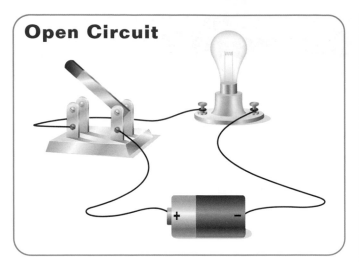

▲ **Figure 10** A bulb in an open circuit will not light because the path for current is not complete.

Over time, the chemicals reacting inside a battery will be used up. When this happens, bulbs in the circuit will go out. To turn a bulb off and on again before a battery runs out, we can add a switch to a circuit. A **switch** is a device that can interrupt electric current in a circuit. When a switch is open, the path for current is interrupted. An **open circuit** is an interrupted electric circuit (Figure 10). A bulb in an open circuit will not light.

Complex circuits can contain many wires, bulbs, and batteries. Describing these circuits can be difficult. Drawing a circuit diagram is easier. A **circuit diagram** uses symbols to represent objects in a circuit (Figures 11 and 12).

Object	Symbol
battery	—┤├—
wire	———
bulb	—Ⓞ—
switch	•—•

▲ **Figure 11** Circuit symbols represent objects in a real circuit.

Circuit Diagram

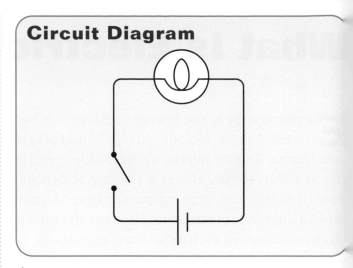

▲ **Figure 12** This circuit diagram shows the same circuit pictured in Figure 10.

Voltage, Resistance, and Current

Although there are some important differences, charges flowing in a circuit can be compared to water circulating at a water park (Figure 13). A pump at the base of a waterslide works against gravity to raise the water up to the top. The water gains **gravitational potential energy** because of its high position. In a circuit, a battery acts like a pump. A battery separates charges, creating a difference in electric potential energy in the circuit. **Electric potential** is the potential energy per unit of electric charge in a circuit. Somewhat like water flowing downhill, charges flow from areas of high potential energy to areas of low potential energy. This difference is known as **potential difference,** or **voltage.** The higher the water at a water park is raised, the greater its gravitational potential energy. Likewise, the greater the voltage a battery supplies to a circuit, the greater the flow of electric current. The SI unit of potential difference is the **volt (V).** (*SI* stands for Système International d'Unités, an international system of measurement.)

How does a battery function as a voltage source? You will read more about different types of batteries on page 16. In general, chemical

▲ **Figure 13** Just as a pump is needed to produce a continuous flow of water in the slide, voltage is required to produce an electric current in a circuit.

reactions inside a battery separate electrons from atoms. The electrons build up in one area of the battery called the negative terminal, which is negatively charged. Positive charge builds up in another area called the positive terminal, which is positively charged. When a battery's positive and negative terminals are connected by wire in a closed circuit, electrons in the wire start to move. Electrons at the negative terminal repel nearby electrons. Electrons in neighboring atoms are pushed along the circuit all the way to the positive terminal of the battery.

Because of the large number of collisions between electrons in a circuit, electrons move at a speed of only about 2 centimeters (about 1 inch) per minute. But the electric energy transferred by the current goes much faster. Current transfers electric energy throughout a closed circuit at almost the speed of light.

Recall that current is the rate at which charge is flowing. The SI unit of current is the **ampere (A),** which is often shortened to *amp.* Current in a circuit depends on the amount of voltage and the resistance. Increasing the voltage applied to a circuit increases the current. Increasing the resistance decreases the current. The SI unit of resistance is the **ohm (Ω).** The type of conducting material and its length, thickness, and temperature all affect the resistance. Long, thin, warm wires have a greater resistance than short, thick, cool wires. The number of devices in the circuit also affects resistance. Suppose a light bulb is added to a circuit. Resistance increases as some of the energy in the circuit is changed into light and heat energy. This causes current in the circuit to decrease.

Current, voltage, and resistance in a circuit are related mathematically. This relationship is called Ohm's law, in honor of its discoverer, Georg Ohm (1789–1854), a German physicist who experimented with current electricity. **Ohm's law** states that the current in a circuit is equal to the voltage divided by the resistance. This equation also can be written using the symbols I for current, V for voltage, and R for resistance:

$$\text{current} = \frac{\text{voltage}}{\text{resistance}} \quad \text{or} \quad I = \frac{V}{R}$$

Recall that, in the SI system, current is measured in the unit amperes (A), voltage in volts (V), and resistance in ohms (Ω). This is the relationship among the three units:

$$1 \text{ ampere (A)} = \frac{1 \text{ volt (V)}}{1 \text{ ohm (Ω)}}$$

This means that 1 ampere (or amp) of current flows when 1 volt of potential difference is applied across 1 ohm of resistance.

◀ **Figure 14**
We can find out how much current flows through any electric appliance, such as this lantern, by applying Ohm's law.

Using Ohm's law, we can solve simple circuit problems. Suppose a lantern uses four 1.5-volt batteries and a 40-ohm bulb (Figure 14). How much current flows through the bulb when the lantern is on? The voltage (V) is 4 × 1.5 V = 6 V. The resistance (R) is 40 Ω. Using the equation I = V/R, we can find the current:

$$I\ (A) = \frac{V\ (V)}{R\ (\Omega)}$$
$$= \frac{6\ V}{40\ \Omega}$$
$$= 0.15\ A$$

When the lantern is turned on, a current of 0.15 amperes flows through the bulb.

We can rearrange the equation I = V/R to find any circuit measurement if we know the other two. For example, we can use the equation below to find the voltage if we know the current and the resistance:

$$V = IR$$

We also can find the amount of resistance of a circuit if we know the voltage and the current by using the following equation:

$$R = \frac{V}{I}$$

Series and Parallel Circuits

Electric circuits can be arranged in two basic ways. In a **series circuit** (Figure 15-A), the current follows only one path. In a **parallel circuit** (Figure 15-B), the current follows multiple paths. Each part of a parallel circuit is called a branch.

Series circuits and parallel circuits work differently. In a series circuit, if a bulb burns out or the switch is open, all the bulbs go out. The burned-out bulb or open switch breaks the current's path, preventing electricity from getting to any of the bulbs. Also, the more bulbs added to a series circuit, the dimmer they shine. This happens because each bulb is a resistor. As resistance increases, current decreases.

In a parallel circuit, if a bulb burns out or a switch on one branch is opened, the other bulbs remain lit. Opening one branch of a parallel circuit does not make the circuit an open circuit. Current can still follow the other branches. Household circuits are parallel so some appliances can be turned off while others can be left on.

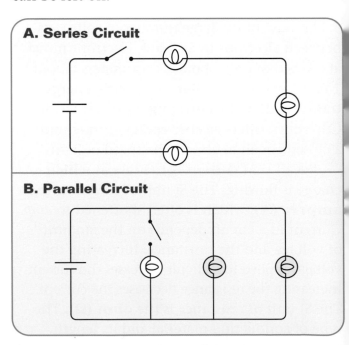

▲ **Figure 15** A series circuit has only one path for current to follow. A parallel circuit has multiple paths.

Electricity and Magnetism

Electromagnetic Force

Electricity and magnetism are closely related. In fact, both are parts of a single electromagnetic force. When an electric current flows through a wire, a magnetic field is created around the wire. When the current stops, the magnetic field disappears. Likewise, a magnetic field can induce an electric current in a wire.

Magnets

A **magnet** (Figure 16) is a material that attracts the metals iron, cobalt, and nickel. These metals, and materials that contain them, are called **ferromagnetic materials.** The pull of a magnet on these materials is called **magnetic force,** or **magnetism.** Some minerals, such as magnetite, are natural magnets. Other magnets are made by people.

Although magnets may have different sizes, shapes, and strengths, all magnets have the same properties. All magnets have two magnetic poles and a magnetic field. The **magnetic poles** are the places on a magnet where its magnetism is the strongest. The **magnetic field** is the space all around a magnet where the magnet's force is exerted.

A bar magnet's poles are at its ends. Usually one pole of a bar magnet is labeled *N* for north-seeking and the other is labeled *S* for south-seeking. If you allow a bar magnet to hang freely from a string, the magnet will turn so that its north-seeking pole points north. Its south-seeking pole will point south.

Just as unlike electric charges attract and like electric charges repel, unlike magnetic poles attract and like magnetic poles repel. An *N* pole and an *S* pole will attract each other. Two *N* poles will repel each other. Two *S* poles will also repel each other.

A magnet's force does not act only at its poles. The magnetic field reaches in all directions around the magnet. Recall that the electric field around a charged object can affect other objects without touching them. A magnetic field acts in a similar way. Because a magnet exerts a force at a distance from the magnet, a magnet can push or pull ferromagnetic objects without touching them.

▲ **Figure 16** No matter what their shape, magnets always have two magnetic poles and a magnetic field.

READ TO UNDERSTAND

- What causes a magnet to be magnetic?

- How can you use electric current to create a magnet?

- How does an electric motor work?

VOCABULARY

magnet	domain
ferromagnetic material	temporary magnet
magnetic force	permanent magnet
magnetism	
magnetic pole	electromagnet
magnetic field	galvanometer
magnetic field lines	electric motor

Magnetic Field Lines

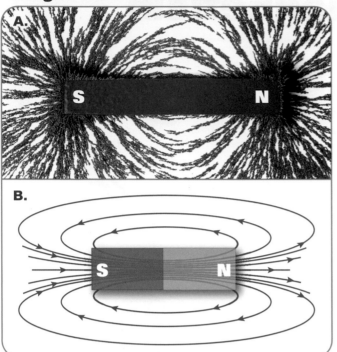

▲ **Figure 17** A magnetic field surrounds a bar magnet in all directions. The iron filings (A) show the field's shape. The field also can be represented by magnetic field lines (B), which show the direction and strength of the field.

Even though we cannot see a magnetic field, we can see its effect. Iron filings sprinkled around a bar magnet form a pattern that shows the shape of the magnetic field (Figure 17-A). The filings gather along invisible lines called **magnetic field lines.** These lines show the direction and strength of the magnetic field (Figure 17-B). The direction of a field line is the direction the *N* pole of a tiny bar magnet would point at that location. The closeness of the lines represents the magnet's strength. Very close field lines represent a stronger field than those that are widely spaced. As you can see, a magnet's force is stronger closer to the magnet and weaker farther away from the magnet.

Magnetism is a result of the way atoms act. Each atom in an object has its own tiny magnetic field. The magnetic fields of the atoms in certain areas line up with one another. These areas are called **domains.** One object can have many domains. Each domain has an *N* pole and an *S* pole.

The domains in a piece of unmagnetized iron or steel point in different directions (Figure 18-A). But when the piece of iron or steel is placed in a strong magnetic field, the domains in the object line up in the same direction (Figure 18-B). Their *N* poles point in one direction, and their *S* poles point in the opposite direction. The piece of iron or steel becomes a magnet.

Some metals are easy to turn into magnets, but their magnetism does not last. In **temporary magnets,** the domains do not stay lined up after the strong magnetic force is removed. Stroking an iron or steel nail with a magnet will make a temporary magnet.

Other metals form lasting, permanent magnets. In **permanent magnets,** the domains stay lined up. If a permanent magnet is cut in two pieces, its domains continue to line up in the same direction. Therefore, the result is two smaller permanent magnets, each with a north and a south pole. A permanent magnet can lose its magnetism if it is hit hard or heated to a high enough temperature. These actions will cause the magnet's domains to point in different directions. The magnet will lose its magnetism.

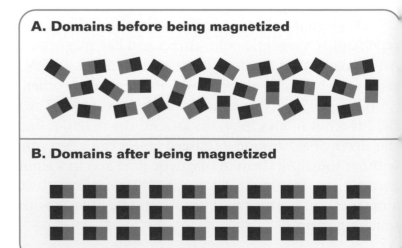

▲ **Figure 18** When a material such as iron or steel is magnetized, its domains line up in the same direction.

Electromagnets

In 1820 the Danish scientist Hans Christian Oersted made a discovery. He saw that an electric current flowing through a wire had an effect on a nearby compass. When the current was switched on and off, the compass needle moved. Oersted concluded that electric currents produce magnetic fields.

Oersted's discovery led to the invention of the electromagnet. An **electromagnet** is a device that becomes a temporary magnet when electric current is supplied to it.

A simple electromagnet can be made by wrapping a wire coil around an iron or steel nail and then connecting both ends of the wire to a battery (Figure 19). Current flows through the wire, creating a magnetic field. The nail becomes a magnet and will attract iron and steel objects. If the wire is disconnected from the battery, the current stops and the nail will no longer attract the objects.

The magnetic field of an electromagnet can be made stronger by increasing the number of wire loops in the coil. Increasing the amount of current flowing through the wire also strengthens an electromagnet.

Telephones use electromagnets to change the sound energy of your voice into electric energy. The electric energy travels along wires and is changed back into sound energy when it reaches the phone on the other end.

Galvanometers

A **galvanometer** is an instrument that measures electric current (Figure 20). A galvanometer contains a wire coil that is placed between the poles of a permanent magnet. When electric current flows through the wire coil, the wire coil becomes an electromagnet. The magnetic field of the wire coil interacts with the magnetic field of the permanent magnet. The attracting and repelling of the magnetic poles of the wire coil and permanent magnet cause the wire coil to rotate. The wire coil is connected to a spring that moves a pointer. The pointer indicates the amount of current by pointing to marks on a scale. The greater the current in the wire, the more the pointer moves.

Electromagnet

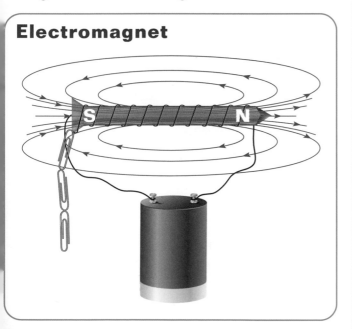

▲ **Figure 19** An electromagnet has the same magnetic properties as a bar magnet. In what ways do electromagnets and bar magnets differ?

Galvanometer

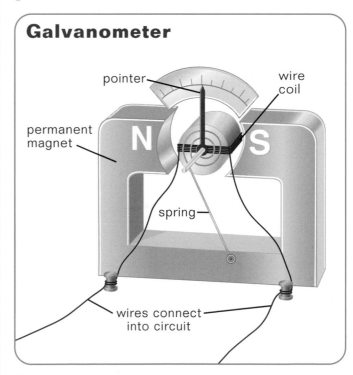

▲ **Figure 20** In a galvanometer, the magnetic field of an electromagnet interacts with the magnetic field of a permanent magnet to indicate the amount of current in a circuit.

Electric Motors

An **electric motor** changes electric energy into kinetic energy, the energy of motion. Like other forms of energy, kinetic energy can be used to do work. Electric motors are all around us. A motor moves the blades of a blender that makes a milk shake. Power tools such as saws and drills have motors. Washers and dryers also have motors.

A simple electric motor has three main parts (Figure 21). The first part is a permanent magnet. The magnet is fixed in one place and cannot move. The second part is a temporary magnet. This is an electromagnetic coil, or electromagnet, that rotates between the poles of the fixed magnet. The third part of a motor is a commutator, a device that changes the direction of the current flowing through the electromagnetic coil.

The four steps near the illustration explain how the three main parts of a motor work together to produce motion. The resulting kinetic energy can be used to turn a rod or axle connected to a wheel, gear, or other device.

Electric Motor

❶ A battery or other power source causes current to flow through a motor's wire coil, creating an electromagnetic field.

❷ The electromagnetic field of the wire coil interacts with the magnetic field of a permanent magnet. The unlike poles of the wire coil and permanent magnet are attracted to each other. The attraction causes the coil to make a half turn so the unlike poles line up.

❸ The commutator changes the direction of the current in the wire coil. The change in current reverses the poles of the wire coil. This causes like poles of the permanent magnet and the wire coil to be near each other. Since like poles repel, the wire loop makes another half turn.

❹ The commutator keeps changing the direction of the current at each half turn. The continuous attracting and repelling of the poles keeps the wire coil turning. The turning coil spins a rod or axle.

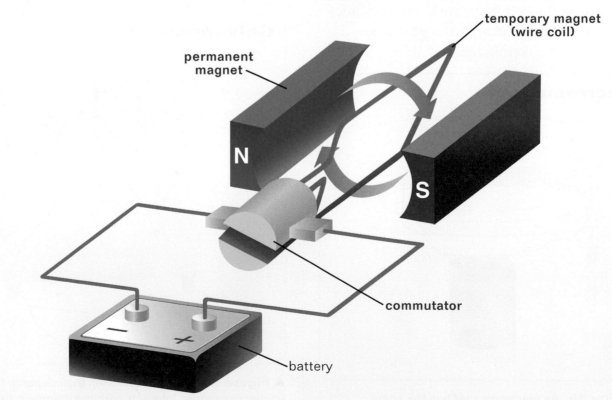

permanent magnet

temporary magnet (wire coil)

N

S

commutator

battery

▲ **Figure 21** A motor converts electric energy into kinetic energy.

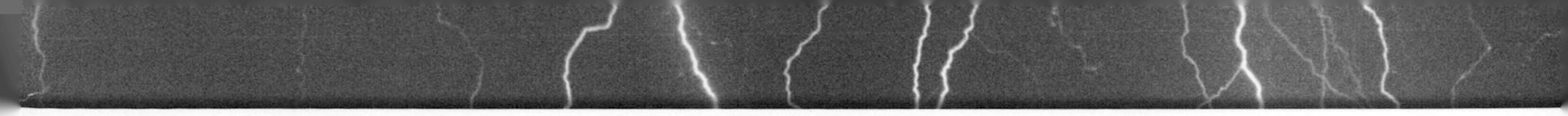

Generating Electric Current

Energy Sources

Electric energy is part of nature. Lightning is a huge discharge of static electricity. Even your muscles and nerves produce small amounts of electric energy. Humans have developed technologies that allow us to convert other types of energy, such as chemical and kinetic, into electric energy. Power plants use the energy in coal, oil, natural gas, water, wind, and the Sun to generate electric current.

Read to Understand

- How are magnetic fields in a generator used to create an electric current?
- How does a flashlight battery produce electric current?
- What is the difference between current from a battery and current from an electric outlet?

VOCABULARY

generator	direct current (DC)
electrochemical cell	alternating current (AC)
dry cell	transformer
wet cell	

Generators

Around 1831 Michael Faraday of England and Joseph Henry of the United States independently conducted experiments to see if a magnetic field could produce an electric current. They moved a magnet through a coil of wire in a closed circuit attached to a galvanometer. The circuit did not have a battery in it. Yet each scientist observed that an electric current was produced in the wire as long as either the coil or the magnet was changing direction, thus changing the magnetic field.

A **generator** is a machine that uses changing magnetic fields to produce electric current. In a power plant, kinetic energy produced by a power source such as a water or wind turbine is changed into electric energy using a generator.

Generators work in different ways. One type of generator moves magnets past coils of wire. Another type of generator makes a wire coil turn within a magnetic field (Figure 22). As long as the wire coil turns or the magnets move, the strength of the magnetic field affecting the coil changes, and a current is produced in the coil.

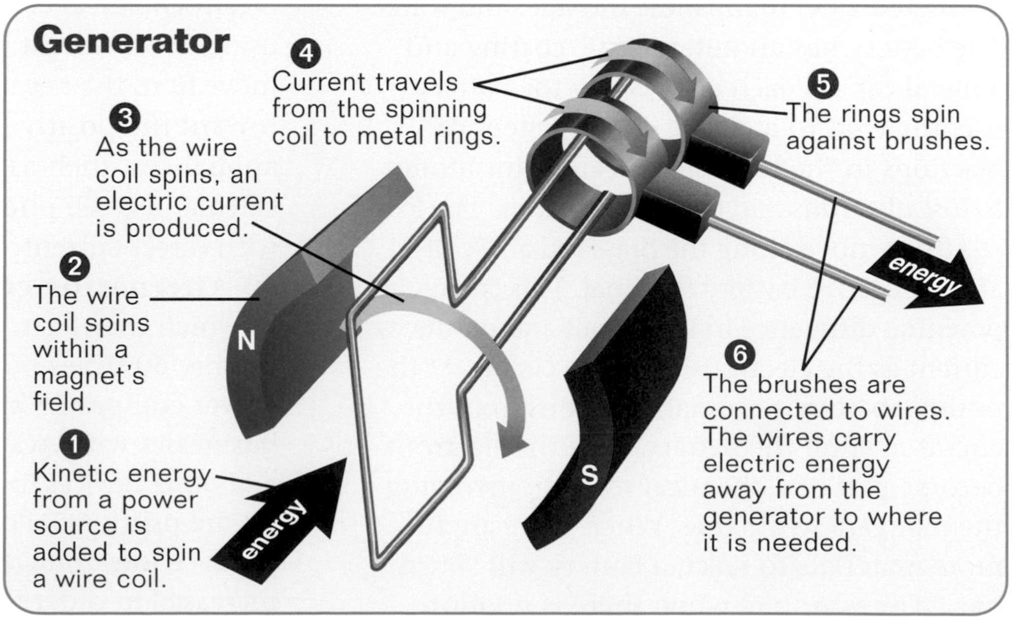
Generator
1 Kinetic energy from a power source is added to spin a wire coil.
2 The wire coil spins within a magnet's field.
3 As the wire coil spins, an electric current is produced.
4 Current travels from the spinning coil to metal rings.
5 The rings spin against brushes.
6 The brushes are connected to wires. The wires carry electric energy away from the generator to where it is needed.
N
S
energy
energy

► **Figure 22**
A generator changes kinetic energy into electric energy.

Electrochemical Cells

Electrochemical cells are devices that supply electric energy through chemical reactions. Two basic types of electrochemical cells are used. A **dry cell** contains pastelike materials that undergo chemical reactions. We use dry cells in many small devices. A **wet cell** contains chemicals in liquid form. Wet cells are used to start car engines, for example.

Both a dry cell and a wet cell have potential energy, or stored energy. When a dry cell or a wet cell is used to push charges in an electric circuit, this energy changes from potential to electric. No energy is lost. The law of conservation of energy says energy cannot be created or destroyed. Energy can only be changed from one form to another.

In electronics, a battery consists of two or more electrochemical cells working together. However, in everyday life, we often use the word *battery* to describe a single electrochemical cell. We use one or more batteries to operate flashlights, radios, and digital cameras.

A common type of dry cell battery is a 1.5-volt alkaline D-cell (Figure 23). This type of disposable battery is used often in flashlights. The battery is made up of a steel can with a brass rod in the center. The can is filled with a moist paste that contains chemicals, including powdered zinc, manganese dioxide, and water. The battery has an outer plastic coating and a metal cap on each end. When the battery is connected to a closed circuit, chemical reactions in the moist paste cause zinc atoms to lose electrons and become zinc ions. The lost electrons move along the brass rod and collect at the negative battery terminal. This creates a potential difference in the circuit and produces current as the electrons enter the circuit. At the positive battery terminal, electrons from the circuit re-enter the battery. Here the electrons become part of a chemical reaction involving the manganese dioxide. When there are no more materials to react, a battery will "burn out." For example, when there is no more

Inside a Battery

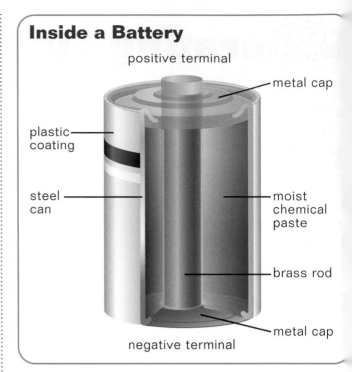

positive terminal

metal cap

plastic coating

steel can

moist chemical paste

brass rod

metal cap

negative terminal

▲ **Figure 23** When a battery is connected in a circuit, chemical reactions take place inside the battery.

zinc left to produce zinc ions, no current is produced. A battery will also burn out if there is no more manganese dioxide left to react.

Two Kinds of Current

Electric current has two forms: direct and alternating. In **direct current (DC)**, electrons move in one direction (Figure 24-A). Electrochemical cells supply electric energy using direct current. The electrons in the circuit move from the negative terminal of the battery toward the positive terminal. Many small appliances, such as portable CD players, calculators, cell phones, and radios, operate with direct current.

Alternating current (AC) is current in which the electrons move back and forth, usually 60 times per second (Figure 24-B). Power companies supply our homes and businesses with AC. When we plug appliances and other devices into household electric outlets, we are using AC. Power station generators produce low-voltage AC. This voltage must be increased in order for AC to be sent from the

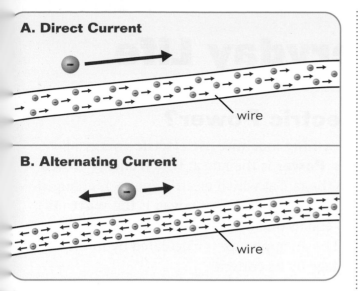

A. Direct Current

wire

B. Alternating Current

wire

▲ **Figure 24** In direct current, electrons move slowly in one direction. In alternating current, electrons vibrate back and forth quickly.

power station through the utility lines. Then the voltage must be decreased before it can be distributed safely from the utility lines into homes, schools, and businesses.

Power companies use **transformers** to increase and decrease the voltage of AC. A transformer has a ferromagnetic core and two separate wire coils (Figure 25). One coil is called the primary coil. It is connected to a source of

alternating current. The other coil is called the secondary coil. Alternating current in the primary coil produces a changing magnetic field. The field acts on the nearby secondary coil. The changing magnetic field produces an alternating current in the secondary coil.

Look at Figure 25 closely. The secondary coil has more wire loops than the primary coil. This type of transformer is called a step-up transformer. In this device, the voltage of the AC in the secondary coil is greater than the voltage of the AC in the primary coil. Power companies use step-up transformers to increase the voltage of AC produced by generators. Transmission lines conduct the high-voltage AC to distribution centers close to cities and towns.

Distribution centers use a step-down transformer to decrease the voltage going from the distribution center to local utility lines. The secondary coil of a step-down transformer has fewer wire loops than the primary coil. As a result, this kind of transformer reduces AC voltage. Step-down transformers are also used along local utility lines to step down the voltage from the line into a house.

Step-Up Transformer

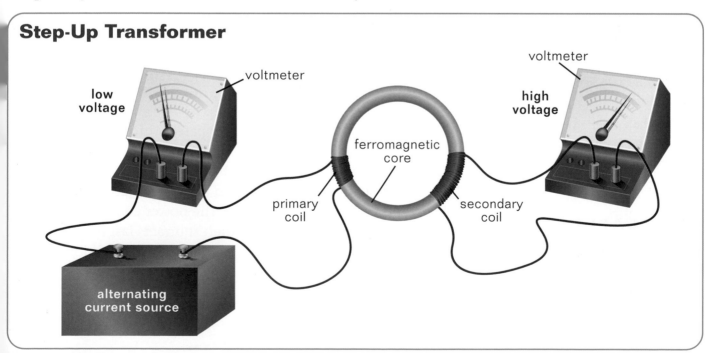

voltmeter

low voltage

voltmeter

high voltage

ferromagnetic core

primary coil

secondary coil

alternating current source

▲ **Figure 25** A step-up transformer increases the voltage of an AC circuit. Instruments called voltmeters show the voltage in the primary coil and the secondary coil.

Electricity in Everyday Life

▲ **Figure 26** A watt-hour meter records the amount of electric energy used in a building.

READ TO UNDERSTAND

- What is electric power?
- What are some ways you can stay safe while using electricity?
- What is the difference between nonrenewable and renewable energy sources?

VOCABULARY

power	electrolyte
electric power	fuse
watt (W)	circuit breaker
kilowatt (kW)	
kilowatt-hour (kWh)	nonrenewable energy source
short circuit	renewable energy source

What Is Electric Power?

A lamp and a washing machine use electric energy at different rates. **Power** is the rate at which energy is used. **Electric power** is the rate at which electric energy is changed to other forms of energy. The SI unit of power is the **watt (W)**. A **kilowatt (kW)** equals one thousand watts.

The power used by an appliance is calculated by multiplying the appliance's voltage by its current:

power = voltage × current

or, in units,

watts (W) = volts (V) × amps (A)

Suppose you have a lamp that uses a compact fluorescent light bulb. If the voltage supplied is 120 volts and the current flowing through the bulb is 0.125 amperes, the bulb is using 15 watts of power: 120 V × 0.125 A = 15 W.

The local power company tracks how much electric energy it supplies to each home or business. The amount of electric energy is equal to the amount of power used multiplied by the time it was used. One **kilowatt-hour (kWh)** is a unit of electric energy equal to the amount of work done by one kilowatt in one hour.

electric energy (kWh) = electric power (kW) × time (hours)

The AC from the power company passes through a watt-hour meter (Figure 26) as it enters each home. Electric current passing through the meter causes a metal disk to spin and dials to turn. The dials show the electric energy in kilowatt-hours that has been delivered to the house. Each month the power company records the meter reading. The company then subtracts last month's reading from this month's reading to determine the amount of electricity used (Figure 27).

▶ **Figure 27** The power company supplied 718 kilowatt-hours of electric energy for the month and charged a fee of $0.091 for each kilowatt-hour used.

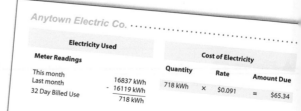

Anytown Electric Co.		
Electricity Used		
Meter Readings		
This month	16837 kWh	
Last month	− 16119 kWh	
32 Day Billed Use	718 kWh	

Cost of Electricity		
Quantity	Rate	Amount Due
718 kWh ×	$0.091 =	$65.34

Using Electricity Safely

Electricity is safe as long as we use it wisely. The table below lists two major safety problems that we have to be aware of when using electricity. The table also lists ways to solve each problem.

▶ **Figure 28**
This plug has a third prong. The plug is safer than a two-pronged plug because the third prong acts as a conductor that grounds the appliance.

Problem	Solution
Short circuit A **short circuit** occurs when current takes a path that is not intended. For example, if the insulation around a wire is worn, current can flow from the wire to another conductor. A short circuit shortens the path of the current and reduces the resistance. Because the resistance is low, the amount of current in the circuit increases. This can cause a fire.	• Never unplug a lamp or appliance by tugging on its cord. Pull on the plug itself. • Do not overload wall outlets or power strips. • The circuits in most buildings are equipped with safety devices that protect against an overload of current. A **fuse** is a device that contains a metal wire that melts, or "blows," when current reaches an unsafe level. When the wire melts, the circuit opens. Once a fuse is blown, the source of the problem must be fixed and the fuse must be replaced. A **circuit breaker** is a device that contains either a special metal strip or an electromagnet. These move a switch that opens the circuit when current reaches an unsafe level. The switch can be reset without having to be replaced.
Becoming part of a circuit Human body cells contain solutions of electrolytes. An **electrolyte** is a compound that forms positive and negative ions when it dissolves in water. These ions can conduct electric current. If the human body accidentally becomes part of a circuit, current will flow through it. Electric current can cause burns. It can also permanently damage the nervous system. It can even cause death.	• Never use an electric appliance when your hands are wet or you are standing in water. • Never touch downed power lines or objects that are in contact with them. • Never stick your finger or any object other than a plug into an electric outlet. • Never use appliances that have broken or frayed wires. • In a thunderstorm, avoid open fields, high places, and tall objects such as trees and poles. Seek shelter inside a large building or an enclosed vehicle. Once inside, avoid touching appliances and metal surfaces. Avoid water-related activities.

Conserving Electricity

Most power plants rely on nonrenewable energy sources to spin the turbines of their generators (see Figure 22, page 15). **Non-renewable energy sources** are resources that cannot be replaced once they are used. The fossil fuels coal, oil, and natural gas are examples of nonrenewable energy sources. Nonrenewable energy sources are limited, yet our usage of them increases each year (Figure 29). Pollution is also a concern. Burning fossil fuels releases soot and gases including carbon dioxide into the atmosphere.

Some power plants use moving water or wind to spin turbines. Water and wind are examples of renewable energy sources. **Renewable energy sources** are energy sources that are replaced naturally. Solar energy, tidal energy, and geothermal energy are other renewable energy sources (Figure 30). We are now developing technologies that make better use of these energy sources. No energy source is perfect, however. Even with renewable energy sources, we must carefully weigh the pros and cons of their cost, availability, and environmental impact.

▲ **Figure 30** The U.S. Department of Energy's Solar Decathlon is an annual competition that takes place in Washington, D.C. Each team builds a house that uses only sunlight as energy. The home shown was built by students from the New York Institute of Technology.

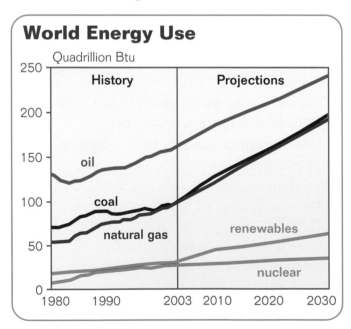

World Energy Use

Quadrillion Btu

| History | Projections |

oil
coal
natural gas
renewables
nuclear

1980 1990 2003 2010 2020 2030

▲ **Figure 29** This chart from the U.S. Department of Energy predicts the world's energy use by fuel type through the year 2030.

By conserving electric energy, we can conserve the resources used to produce it. The following are some ways you can conserve energy at home. Discuss any changes with your family first. Turn off lights, televisions, and computers when they are not being used. Use compact fluorescent light bulbs instead of incandescent bulbs. Use energy-efficient appliances. Run dishwashers only with a full load and air-dry dishes instead of using the drying cycle. Wash only full loads of clothes and clean dryer lint filters after each load. Lower your water heater setting to about 49°C (about 120°F). Use low-flow showerheads. Seal leaks around windows and doors. Check and clean air conditioner filters monthly. Use programmable thermostats that lower the temperature when you are away or sleeping.

Joseph Henry (1797–1878)

Joseph Henry was born in Albany, New York. In 1819 he entered Albany Academy, a day school for boys in elementary grades through college. He returned to the school in 1826 as a professor of mathematics and science.

During his career, Joseph Henry investigated how magnetic fields and electric currents interact. Henry also developed the principle of the telegraph. He placed an electromagnet and a movable iron rod near a bell. Then he ran wires from the electromagnet to an electrochemical cell in another room. Opening and closing the circuit made the electromagnet move the rod back and forth, striking the bell. Samuel Morse used Henry's idea to cause a pendulum holding a pencil to strike a strip of paper. This striking action created a coded message of dots and dashes. Morse generally is credited with inventing the telegraph.

Henry also developed new ways to increase electromagnets' strength. In 1831 he constructed the most amazing electromagnet of its time (Figure 32). A year later, Henry became a professor at Princeton University in New Jersey. Besides teaching, he continued to conduct research.

In 1846 Henry became the first secretary of the Smithsonian Institution in Washington, D.C. At that time, many people thought the main purpose of science was to invent devices that make life easier and industry more profitable. But Henry believed the purpose of science was to study and gather knowledge about the world. He realized that this basic research often led to practical applications.

During his 32 years at the Smithsonian, Henry helped establish the National Weather Service. He was science adviser to U.S. presidents and supported the work of many inventors, including Alexander Graham Bell. He also was president of the National Academy of Sciences.

▲ **Figure 31** U.S. scientist Joseph Henry once wrote, "The discovery of today, which appears unconnected with any useful process, may, in the course of a few years, become the fruitful source of a thousand inventions."

▲ **Figure 32** This is the powerful electromagnet built by Joseph Henry for Yale University in 1831. It weighs 27 kilograms (59.5 pounds) and can support a weight of 935.7 kilograms (2,063 pounds).

About Superconductors

Some materials lose their electrical resistance when they are cooled to very low temperatures. With no resistance, these very cold materials conduct electric current better than other materials. These materials are called superconductors. A superconductor is a perfect conductor. Current flows through a superconductor with no loss of energy.

A superconductor also keeps magnetic fields from entering it. A superconductor can lift a magnet and keep it there (Figure 33). Because the magnet seems to float, or levitate, the lift is called magnetic levitation, or Maglev.

How does this happen? When a magnet is brought close to a superconductor, small electric currents form on the surface of the superconductor. These supercurrents produce a magnetic field around the superconductor. This magnetic field repels the magnetic field of the magnet.

▲ **Figure 34** A Maglev train glides along a track at a railroad research center in Japan.

Some high-speed express trains use superconductors. A type of Maglev train has onboard superconductors (Figure 34). These superconductors repel electromagnets along the track. As a result, the train is lifted just above the track. Because there is no friction from the track, the trains can reach speeds of 500 kilometers (about 310 miles) per hour.

Superconductors are also used in medicine and computer technology. Magnetic resonance imaging (MRI) machines use superconductors, radio waves, and computers to produce images of the tissues inside a person's body. Doctors can study these images to diagnose conditions involving the muscles, nerves, and brain. The superconducting magnets used inside MRI scanners are extremely powerful. Patients must remove any metal objects, such as jewelry and eyeglasses, before entering the scan room.

▲ **Figure 33** A magnet floats, or levitates, above a very cold superconductor.

Glossary

A page number in boldface type indicates the page on which the word is defined in the text.

alternating current (AC) current in which the electrons move back and forth (**16**, 17)

ampere (A) SI unit of current; often called an *amp* (**9**, 10)

atom tiny building blocks that make up all matter (**2**, 3, 9, 12, 16)

battery device that converts chemical energy to electric energy or a group of such devices operating together; also called an *electrochemical cell*; see also *dry cell, wet cell* (**7**–9, 10, 13, 15, 16)

charging by conduction touching a charged object to a neutral object in order to charge the neutral object (**4**)

charging by friction rubbing a neutral material with another neutral material in order to charge them (**4**)

charging by induction bringing a charged object near a neutral object in order to charge the neutral object (**4**)

circuit breaker device that contains either a special metal strip or an electromagnet that moves a switch to open a circuit when electric current reaches an unsafe level (**19**)

circuit diagram picture that uses symbols to show how objects in a circuit are connected (**8**)

closed circuit complete path along which electric current flows (**7**, 9, 15, 16)

conductor material through which electric current passes easily (**3**–7, 19)

direct current (DC) current in which the electrons move in one direction (**16**)

domain area in a magnet or in a material that is attracted to a magnet where the magnetic fields of the atoms line up with one another (**12**)

dry cell electrochemical cell that contains paste-like materials that undergo chemical reactions to generate electricity (**16**)

electric charge basic property of matter; can be negative or positive (**2**, 5, 7, 8, 11)

electric circuit path for electric current (**7**, 8, 16)

electric current steady, or continuous, flow of charge (**7**–9, 11, 13, 15, 16, 18–22)

electric energy energy a charge has because it is in an electric field or electric current (**2**, 7, 9, 13–16, 18, 20)

electric field space around a charged object where electric force acts (**3**, 7, 11)

electric force force that causes charged materials or objects to attract or repel each other (**3**, 4)

electric motor device that uses magnets to change electric energy into kinetic energy (**14**)

electric potential potential energy per unit of electric charge in a circuit (**8**)

electric power rate at which electric energy is changed to other forms of energy (**18**)

electrochemical cell device that converts chemical energy to electric energy; also called a *battery*; see also *dry cell, wet cell* (**16**, 21)

electrolyte compound that forms positive and negative ions when it dissolves in water (**19**)

electromagnet temporary magnet made when electric current flows through a wire wrapped around an iron or steel core (**13**, 14, 21, 22)

electron one of the three main particles that make up atoms; has a negative charge (**2**–6, 16)

electroscope instrument that detects electric charge (**5**)

ferromagnetic material material that is attracted to a magnet: iron, cobalt, nickel, or material that contains these metals (**11**)

fuse device that contains a metal wire that melts, or "blows," and opens a circuit when electric current reaches an unsafe level (**19**)

galvanometer instrument that detects electric current (**13**)

generator device that uses magnets to change kinetic energy into electric energy (**15**, 17, 20)

gravitational potential energy stored energy (**8**)

grounding connecting an object to Earth with a conductor (**6**)

induced charge area of charge caused by induction (**4**)

insulator material through which electric current does not pass easily (**3**–7)

ion atom with a net positive or net negative charge (**2**, 16, 19)

kilowatt (kW) unit of electric power equal to 1,000 watts (**18**)

kilowatt-hour (kWh) unit of electric energy equal to the work done by one kilowatt in one hour (**18**)

lightning naturally occurring, rapid, and powerful static discharge (**6**, 7, 15)

lightning rod device that protects buildings from lightning strikes by providing a grounded path for the static discharge (**6**)

magnet material that attracts the metals iron, cobalt, and nickel (**11**–15, 21, 22)

magnetic field space around a magnet where the magnet's force acts (**11**, 12, 13, 15, 17, 21, 22)

magnetic field lines invisible lines that show the direction and strength of a magnetic field; also called *lines of force* (**12**)

magnetic force pull of a magnet on ferromagnetic materials; often called *magnetism* (**11**, 12)

magnetic pole one of two places on a magnet where magnetic force is the strongest (**11**, 13)

magnetism another term for *magnetic force* (**11**, 12)

neutron one of the three main particles that make up atoms; has no charge (**2**, 3)

nonrenewable energy source energy source that cannot be replaced once it is used (**20**)

nucleus center of an atom, made up of protons and neutrons (**2**, 3)

ohm (Ω) SI unit of resistance (**9**, 10)

Ohm's law statement that the current in a circuit equals the voltage divided by the resistance (**9**, 10)

open circuit interrupted electric circuit through which current cannot flow (**8**)

parallel circuit electric circuit in which the current follows multiple paths (**10**)

permanent magnet magnet that holds its magnetic properties for a long time because its domains stay lined up (**12**–14)

potential difference measure of the change in electric energy per electron from one point to another; also called *voltage* (**8**, 9, 16)

power rate at which energy is used (14–**18**, 19, 20)

proton one of the three main particles that make up atoms; has a positive charge (**2**, 3, 5, 6)

renewable energy source energy source that is replaced naturally (**20**)

resistance measure of a material's ability to limit the flow of electric current (**7**, 9, 10, 19, 22)

resistor device that resists the flow of current and changes electric energy into another form of energy (**7**)

separation of charge rearrangement of electrons on an object (**4**, 6)

series circuit electric circuit in which the current follows only one path (**10**)

short circuit condition that occurs when electric current takes a path that is not intended (**19**)

static charge excess positive or negative electric charge on a material or object (**3**, 6)

static discharge loss of static charge (**6**)

static electricity term commonly used to describe the buildup of charge on an object (**3**, 15)

switch device that can interrupt the path for electric current in a circuit (**8**, 9)

temporary magnet magnet that loses its magnetism after a short time because its domains do not stay lined up (**12**–14)

transformer device that changes the voltage of alternating current (**17**)

volt (V) SI unit of potential difference (**8**–10, 16)

voltage measure of the change in electric energy per electron from one point to another; also called *potential difference* (**8**–10, 16–18)

watt (W) SI unit of power (**18**, 19)

wet cell electrochemical cell that contains a liquid that undergoes chemical reactions to generate electricity (**16**)